Comic Capers

DESPERATE DAN

BEANO**books**
geddes & grosset

West World

Dan's Gals

© D.C. Thomson & Co., Ltd 2000

Published 2000 by BEANObooks geddes&grosset ,
an imprint of Children's Leisure Products Limited,
David Dale House, New Lanark ML11 9DJ, Scotland

ISBN 1 84205 004 4

Printed and bound in Italy

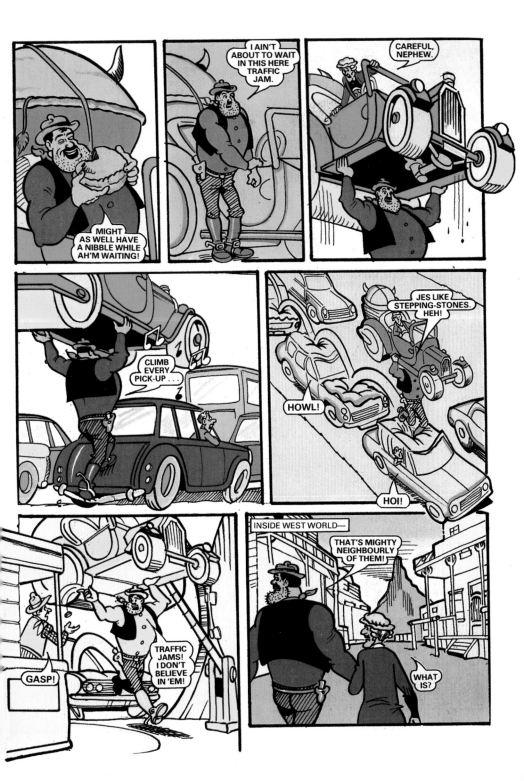

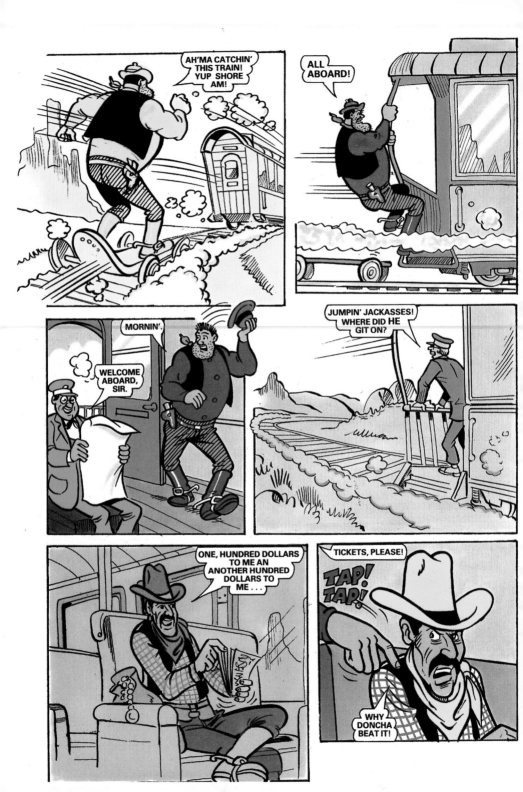

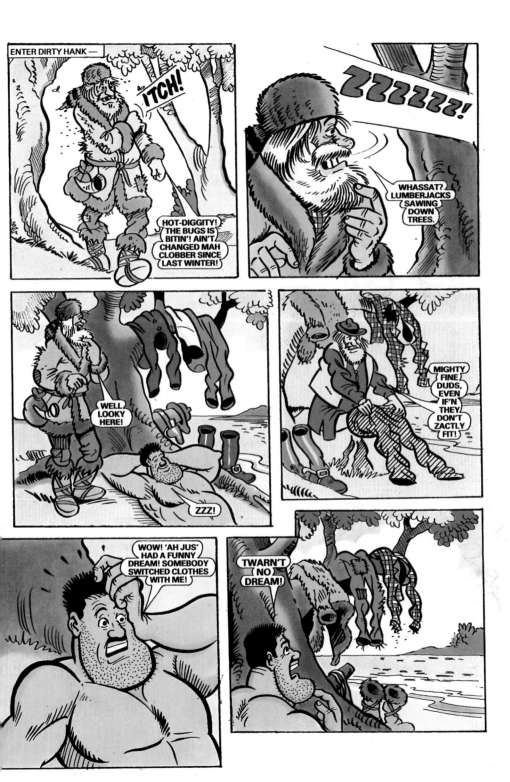

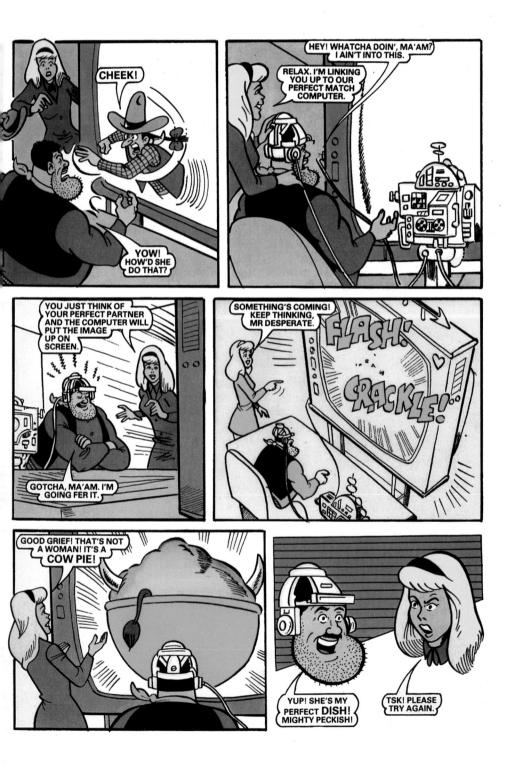

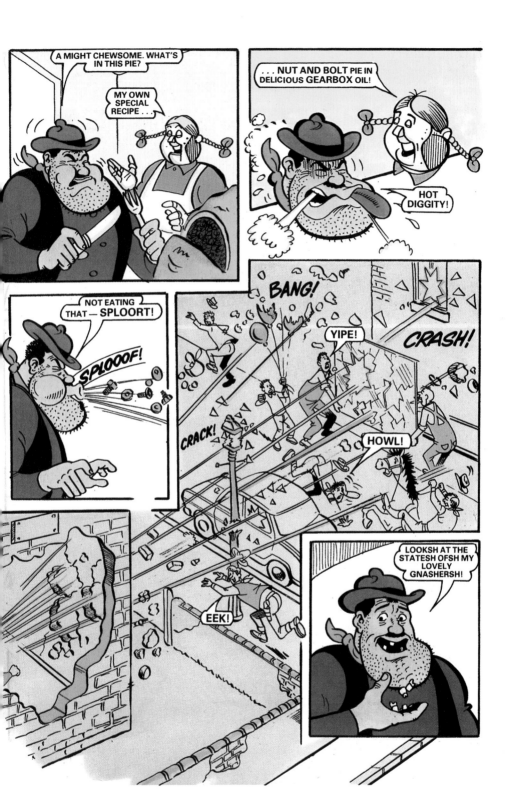

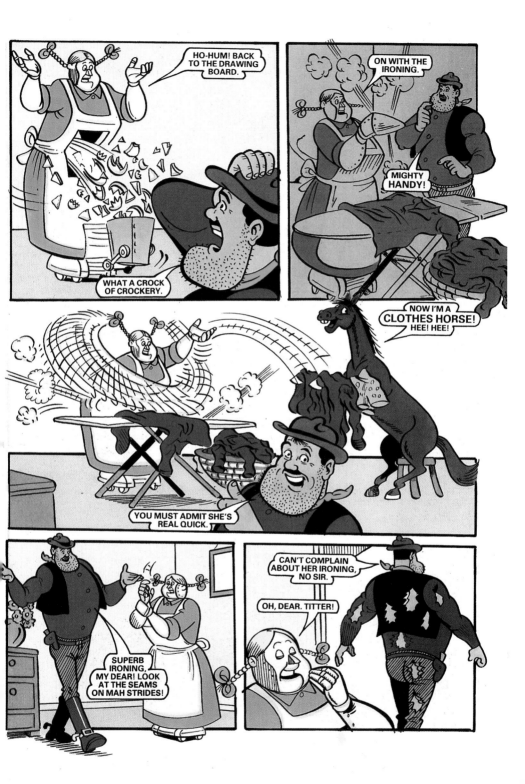

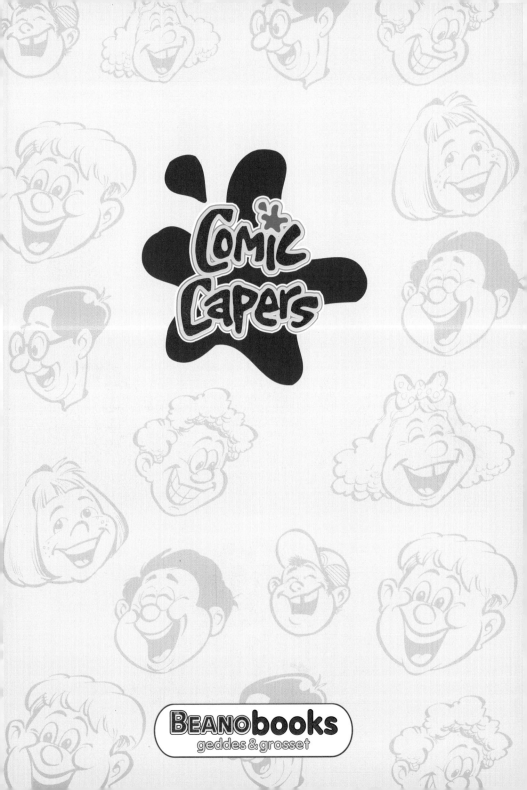